Contents

C000097497

Teachers' notes

Introduction

The activities in this book aim to support the implementation of Reading, and Speaking and Listening in the National Curriculum for English at Key Stage 1. They are not designed as teaching tools in themselves but rather they offer children the opportunity to practise newly-acquired skills. In order to gain the maximum benefit from these activities, it is essential that they are incorporated into an environment which offers time for talking, listening, thinking, telling, reading and writing.

There is always the danger with photocopiable sheets that children will see them simply as time-fillers or 'colouring activities'. Always explain the purpose of the activity to them so that they concentrate on that aspect of the task.

The aims of this book

The aims of this book are:
• to encourage young readers to sequence logically connected events;
• to become familiar with the conventions of reading sequenced texts in order to adopt this attention to logic into their own writing;
• to offer opportunities to consider different possible endings so that the child comes to recognise that stories have beginnings, developments and conclusions;

• to offer different types of texts for simple sequencing: nursery rhymes, original stories, traditional tales and non-fiction;
• to extend the children's understanding of themselves and the environment in which they live, for example by investigating the seasons, growing up and recycling paper;
• to offer opportunities to work in collaboration with a partner in order to discuss the probable order of events and in this way to clarify their own understanding of causal connections;
• to present children with a variety of texts using a range of grammatical connectives which they should then transfer into their own writing.

The value of teaching story sequencing

Children find it difficult to tell or write a connected narrative successfully. Too often they begin a narrative which is quite obviously not at the real beginning. This is not surprising as children are attracted to the dramatic features of the story and bypass the less interesting albeit necessary scene-setting required by their audience. Similarly, children will forget to follow a narrative through to its logical conclusion and either the end of the story peters out or is extended beyond the attention span of most listeners.

In order to gain confidence and experience, it is best to build upon a child's own sense of sequence acquired through the patterning of well-known rhymes and traditional tales. Even very young children recognise that 'the fox ate up every bit of the little gingerbread boy' is the end of a story. For this reason, the activities in this book include nursery rhymes, traditional tales, well-known stories and Aesop's fables.

As a preparation for sequencing, children should be encouraged to retell stories orally and to recount events that they know or have experienced. In order to keep the child 'on task' and to help her present her story in a logical order, she is likely to need gentle guidance in the retelling through comments and questions. Some older children may benefit from you role-modelling how to retell a simple event, for example, 'Do you remember that we went to look in the school pond? First we put on our coats and then we lined up by the door. Then we crossed the playground....' As a result of this modelling, children will become more aware of the needs of their audience and the vital part that the sequence of events has to play in our lives.

The sequencing activities in this book have been presented in order of difficulty.

Picture sequences

Take time to discuss the contents of the pictures with the children. Encourage them to discuss which picture should be the first before organising the whole sequence. Check that all the children can justify their choice of order. There is no specifically correct order to the events drawn but there is a more likely one.

Ask the children to colour the pictures before they cut them out – once they have been cut out the thin strips of paper are likely to tear if the children try to colour them. The pictures have been kept as simple as possible to help the children keep within the lines when they are colouring.

Pages 5 to 8: Picture sequencing

The content of these four pages has been chosen to reflect situations with which most children will be familiar.
• Wrapping a present
• My lunch box
• Going swimming
• Feeding the cat

Suggestions

Encourage discussion by letting the children work in pairs with a sheet each. Let them colour and cut up the pictures, then put them into sequential order. Then ask the children to tell the story.

Extension activities

• Let the children stick the pictures into their own books or folders.
• Encourage them to add their own text according to their ability.
• Show the children how to make the pictures into a small book, for example using a zig-zag format.
• Stick the pictures on to card and re-use them as a language activity.

Pages 9 to 12: Nursery rhyme sequencing

Some children may find text sequencing easier than pictures. Let the children physically move the sentences around and read them aloud to a friend as this helps them to recognise inconsistencies. These four rhymes have been selected because of their popularity.
• Humpty Dumpty
• Jack and Jill
• Little Jack Horner
• Little Bo-Peep

Suggestions

Make sure that the children are familiar with the selected rhyme. Let them work in pairs with a sheet each to colour the pictures, cut them out and place them in sequential order.

Make a class rhyme book. Ask the children what rhymes they know. Collect these and write them on to the board or a large sheet of paper.

Encourage the children to learn some of the poems by heart. Ask them to join in with you. As they become more confident, see if you can stop and the children carry on with the verse.

Quiz the children on the rhymes that they know, for example, 'What is the line after this one? How does this rhyme end? What comes before this line, eg "And Jill came tumbling after"?'

Extension activities

• Let the children stick the pictures into their own books or folders.
• Encourage them to add their own text according to their ability.
• Show the children how to make the pictures into a small book, for example using a zig-zag format.
• Stick the pictures on to card and re-use them as a language activity.

Pages 13 to 16: What happens next?

These pages offer children the chance to choose from two alternative endings.
• Rags and the cat
• I want some sweets
• Mother hen
• The spaceship

Suggestions

Let the children work in pairs, with a sheet each, and discuss which ending they prefer. When they have chosen an ending, ask them to colour, cut and sequence the drawings as they choose.

Ask the children to consider some situations and decide what they would do. For example, when playing in the garden do you let your baby brother join in or not? When having breakfast who should have the free cereal toy? Who should choose what to watch on the TV?

Extension activity

Let the children offer an alternative ending of their own.

Pages 17 to 20: Picture and text sequencing

These slightly more difficult sequencing activities require the children to read carefully through all the text and to look for clues within the pictures before deciding upon the correct order. The sentences which come first and last are marked to help the order. Many children need to move the strips around physically before coming to a final decision. This activity involves a considerable amount of reading and rereading and can help to consolidate reading for meaning.

These sentences also offer an opportunity to show the children the pointers to be found with sequential texts, eg first..., then..., now....
• Making a go-kart
• Camping
• A trip to the museum
• The wildlife park

Suggestions

Let the children work in pairs with a sheet each. Ask them to read the sentences, cut them up and then discuss and decide on an appropriate sequential order.

Before allowing the children to stick the sentence strips on to a template or page, it is advisable to check the accuracy of their sequencing.

Extension activities

• Ask the children to colour the pictures and stick the sentence strips into their own books or folders.
• Let the children make the sentence strips into an individual book.
• Stick sentence strips on to card and re-use them as a language activity.

Pages 21 to 23: Text sequencing

These three activities all have a science theme and may be usefully linked to classroom work on science.

• The seasons
• Growing up
• Recycling paper

Suggestions

Use the first activity to encourage the children to talk about the seasons and the months of the year.

A way of helping the children to sequence the months correctly is to play 'When is your birthday?' All the children stand in a circle and chant the months of the year. As their month is named any child whose birthday falls in that month ducks down and stays there until 'December' when all the children should be crouching down. On the repeat they stand up as their month is named.

Pages 24 to 27: Well-known tales

It is important to familiarise children with these stories before giving them this activity. This is best done by telling the story in your own words or reading them from a text.
• The hare and the tortoise
• The lion and the mouse
• Cinderella
• Jack and the beanstalk

Suggestions

These sheets require the reader to write a caption text and do a drawing in order to complete the story. Encourage the children to decide what they will write in the space provided before they colour and cut up the page.

Extension activities

• Encourage the children to compare their endings and discuss the different ways they have written the caption texts.
• Let the children write their own version of a well-known story, offering text followed by illustration.

Pages 28 to 29: Modern tales

• Rocky the robot and the spaceship
• Rocky the robot and the supermarket
These two stories provide practice in sequencing sentences. The order of these sentences is not correct on the page. Ask the children to cut them up and then decide the order. When they are happy that the story makes sense, let them stick them into their books.

Pages 29 to 32: Paragraph sequencing

These need to be physically cut up and re-arranged until the child is happy with the sequence. These are suitable for the child who is a confident Level 2 reader.
• The fox and the crow

- The wind and the sun
- The oak tree and the fir tree

Suggestions

The order of these paragraphs is not correct on the page. To promote discussion, let the children work in pairs. Encourage them to cut up the page and arrange the paragraphs in the order that they think makes sense. Before pasting it into their books, ask them to read it to a partner.

National Curriculum: English

The activities in this book support the following requirements of the PoS for KS1 for the National Curriculum for English:

Speaking and listening
- Pupils should be given opportunities to talk for a range of purposes, including:
  - telling stories, both real and imagined; ... reading and listening to nursery rhymes and poetry, learning some by heart; reading aloud;
  - making simple, clear explanations of choices; giving reasons for opinions;
- They should be taught to incorporate relevant detail in explanations, descriptions and narratives, and to distinguish between the essential and the less important, taking into account the needs of their listeners.

Reading
- Pupils should be introduced to and should read information;
- They should also be taught to use ... their understanding of grammatical structure and the meaning of the text as a whole to make sense of print;
- Within a balanced and coherent programme, pupils should be taught to use the following knowledge, understanding and skills:
  - **Contextual understanding**, focusing on meaning derived from the text as a whole. In order to confirm the sense of what they read, pupils should be taught to use their knowledge of book conventions, story structure, patterns of language and presentational devices;
- In understanding and responding to stories and poems, pupils should be given opportunities to:
  - say what might happen next in a story;
  - retell stories;
- Pupils should be given opportunities to consider the characteristics and features of different kinds of texts, *eg beginnings and endings in stories.*

Writing
- Pupils should be given opportunities to write in response to a variety of stimuli;
- They should be taught to differentiate between print and pictures.

Scottish 5-14 Curriculum: English language

Attainment outcome	Strand	Attainment target	Level
Reading	Reading for information	Find, with teacher support, items of information from an informational text.	A
	Reading for enjoyment	Pupils read for enjoyment simple stories supported by pictures.	A
	Reading to reflect on the writer's ideas and craft	Pupils will read and with teacher support, talk about a short, straightforward text showing that they understand one important idea.	A
Writing	Handwriting	Pupils form letters and space words legibly for the most part.	A
	Imaginative writing	Pupils will write a brief imaginative story.	A

See inside back cover for Northern Ireland Curriculum links

Wrapping a present

Colour the pictures. Cut them out and make a story.

My lunch box

Colour the pictures. Cut them out and make a story.

Going swimming

Colour the pictures. Cut them out and make a story.

Feeding the cat

Colour the pictures. Cut them out and make a story.

Humpty Dumpty

Colour the pictures. Cut them out.
Put them in order and make the rhyme.

Humpty Dumpty had a great fall.

Couldn't put Humpty together again.

Humpty Dumpty sat on the wall.

All the king's horses and all the king's men

Jack and Jill

Colour the pictures. Cut them out.
Put them in order and make the rhyme.

To fetch a pail of water.

Jack fell down and broke his crown

Jack and Jill went up the hill

And Jill came tumbling after.

Little Jack Horner

Colour the pictures. Cut them out.
Put them in order and make the rhyme.

He put in his thumb and pulled out a plum

Little Jack Horner sat in the corner

Eating his Christmas pie.

What a good boy am I.

And said, 'What a good boy am I.'

Little Bo-Peep

Colour the pictures. Cut them out.
Put them in order and make the rhyme.

Leave them alone and they'll come home

And doesn't know where to find them.

Bringing their tails behind them.

Little Bo-Peep has lost her sheep

Rags and the cat

What happens next?

Copy the sentences to make the story.
Choose the ending you like best.
Make up the last sentence yourself.

1 _____

2 _____

3 _____

4 _____

I want some sweets

What happens next?

Copy the sentences to make the story.
Choose the ending you like best.
Make up the last sentence yourself.

1 _____

2 _____

3 _____

4 _____

Mother hen

What happens next?

Copy the sentences to make the story.
Choose the ending you like best.
Make up the last sentence yourself.

1 _____

2 _____

3 _____

4 _____

The spaceship

What happens next?

Copy the sentences to make the story.
Choose the ending you like best.
Make up the last sentence yourself.

1 _____

2 _____

3 _____

4 _____

Making a go-kart

Read the sentences and cut them out.
Put them in order, then stick them into your book.

They found an old box, some bits of wood, some wheels and some nails.

Tom and Harry were going to make a go-kart. They drew some plans.

Harry pushed the go-kart. Tom turned the steering wheel.

Crash! The go-kart fell to pieces. 'Oh, no!' said Tom and Harry.

It took them a long time to make the go-kart.

At last the go-kart was finished. Tom got in to have a ride.

● **Name** _____

Camping

Read the sentences and cut them out.
Put them in order, then stick them into your book.

They woke up.
They were very wet.

The children put up a tent
in the garden.

They had supper.
They were having a lovely time.

'Can we sleep in the tent tonight?'
they asked.
'Yes,' said Mum.

They ran into the house.
Mum made them hot drinks.

In the night it started to rain.
It rained and rained.

Name _____

A trip to the museum

Read the sentences and cut them out.
Put them in order, then stick them into your book.

Lucy jumped with surprise.
The dinosaur winked again
and moved his tail.

Lucy walked into the museum.
She wanted to see the
dinosaurs.

Lucy was going on a school trip
to the museum.

They went to the museum
in a coach.

She looked at the dinosaurs and
one winked at her.

The teacher laughed.
'Don't worry,' he said.
'The models work like robots.'

The wildlife park

Read the sentences and cut them out.
Put them in order, then stick them into your book.

Then they drove to the monkey park.
Peter couldn't see any monkeys.

First they looked at the lions.
Then they looked at the zebras.

Peter was happy.
He was going to the wildlife park
with his family.

'Oh dear, I hope it doesn't rain
on the way home,' said Mum.

They all laughed, but the monkey
ran away with the
windscreen-wiper.

Suddenly a monkey jumped
down from a tree.
He landed on the car.

The seasons

Read the sentences below. Cut them out.
Match the sentences to the pictures.

✂ - - - - - - - - - - - - - - - - - -
In summer the sun feels hot.
There is more daylight.
We can play outside.

In winter it gets dark early.
The weather is cold.
We need to keep warm.

In spring flowers and trees
start to grow.
It begins to get warmer.

In autumn, leaves fall from
the trees.
It begins to get colder.

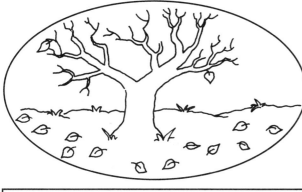

Growing up

Read the sentences below. Cut them out.
Match the sentences to the pictures.

✂ - - - - - - - - - - - - - - - - - - -
I move slowly and my hair is
going grey. I enjoy seeing my
grandchildren.

- - - - - - - - - - - - - - - - - - -
I cannot walk or talk yet.
I drink a lot of milk.
I cry when I am hungry.

- - - - - - - - - - - - - - - - - - -
I can run and jump and I talk
a lot. I can feed myself. I like
playing with my friends.

- - - - - - - - - - - - - - - - - - -
Now I am grown up I can go
to work.
I can drive a car.

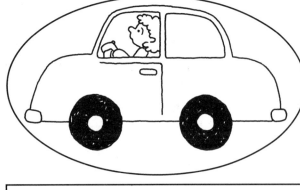

Recycling paper

Read the sentences below. Cut them out.
Match the sentences to the pictures.

✂ ┌─────────────────────────┐
│ We take the bundles to the
│ lorry. The lorry takes the
│ paper to the factory.
└─────────────────────────┘

┌─────────────────────────┐
│ We can use the paper again
│ to write our letters.
└─────────────────────────┘

┌─────────────────────────┐
│ We save our newspapers.
│ We tie them into bundles.
└─────────────────────────┘

┌─────────────────────────┐
│ At the factory the paper is
│ recycled.
└─────────────────────────┘

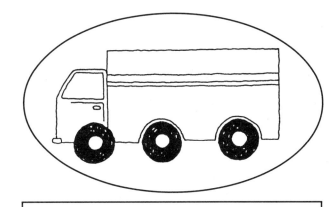

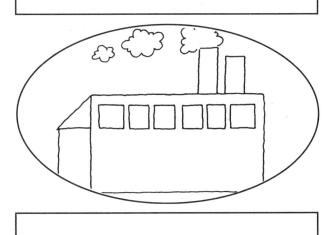

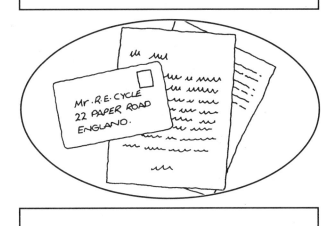

The hare and the tortoise

The ending of the story is missing. Can you finish it?

1
A hare and a tortoise decided to have a race.

2

3
The hare had a rest. He sat down under the tree and fell fast asleep.

4
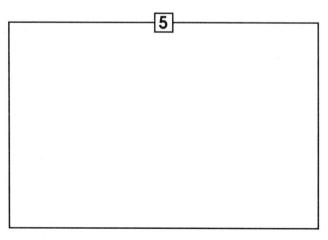

Write what happens.   Draw the end of the story.

5

6

The lion and the mouse

The ending of the story is missing. Can you finish it?

`I am the strongest animal in the jungle!' said the lion.

`I can help you,' said the mouse.
`You are too small to help me,' said the lion.

Draw the end of the story.

Write what happens.

● Name _____

Cinderella

The ending of the story is missing. Can you finish it?

2

Cinderella couldn't go
to the ball.
The ugly sisters went
without her.
Cinderella cried.

4

Cinderella danced with
the prince at the ball.
She was very happy, but
she had to leave at
midnight.

Draw the end of the story.   Write what happens.

5

6

● Name _____

Jack and the beanstalk

The ending of the story is missing. Can you finish it?

2	
The next morning Jack saw a beanstalk growing into the sky. He climbed and climbed to the very top.	

4

Jack waited until the
giant was asleep.
He took the hen and
ran off and climbed down
the beanstalk.

Draw the end of the story.   Write what happens.

5

6

Rocky the robot and the spaceship

Cut out the sentences. Put them in order to tell the story.

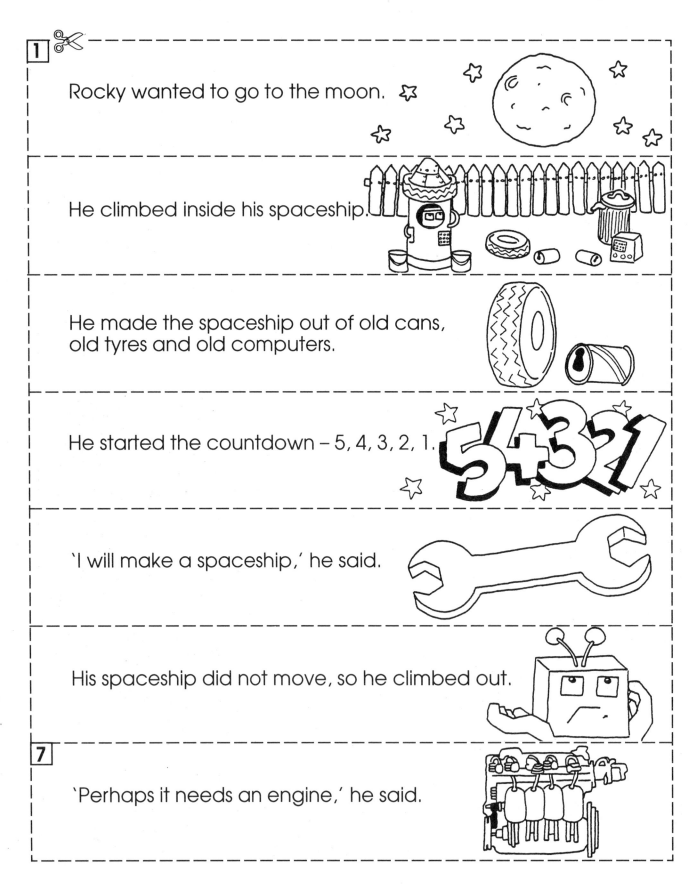

1 Rocky wanted to go to the moon.

He climbed inside his spaceship.

He made the spaceship out of old cans, old tyres and old computers.

He started the countdown – 5, 4, 3, 2, 1.

'I will make a spaceship,' he said.

His spaceship did not move, so he climbed out.

7 'Perhaps it needs an engine,' he said.

Name _____

Rocky the robot and the supermarket

Cut out the sentences. Put them in order to tell the story.

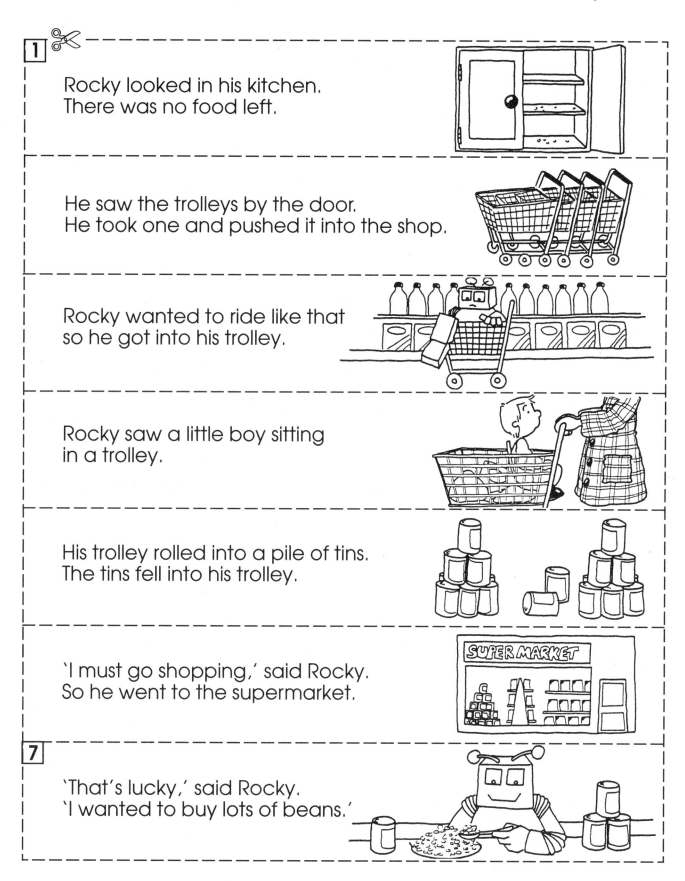

1 | Rocky looked in his kitchen.
There was no food left.

He saw the trolleys by the door.
He took one and pushed it into the shop.

Rocky wanted to ride like that
so he got into his trolley.

Rocky saw a little boy sitting
in a trolley.

His trolley rolled into a pile of tins.
The tins fell into his trolley.

'I must go shopping,' said Rocky.
So he went to the supermarket.

7 | 'That's lucky,' said Rocky.
'I wanted to buy lots of beans.'

Name _____

The fox and the crow

Colour the pictures. Cut out the paragraphs.
Put them in order to tell the story.

The piece of cheese fell on to the ground.
The fox gobbled up the cheese and ran away
leaving the foolish crow without any.

The crow was very pleased.
She opened her beak to sing to the fox.

1

One day a crow found a piece of cheese.
She picked it up in her beak and
flew with it into a tree.

The fox thought of a clever plan.
'Why how beautiful you are,' he said to the crow.
'I am sure that you can sing very well too.'

A cunning fox saw the crow.
He wanted the cheese for his supper but
he knew the crow would not give him any.

The wind and the sun

Colour the pictures. Cut out the paragraphs.
Put them in order to tell the story.

'Now it is my turn,' said the sun
and he began to shine.
It got hotter and hotter.

The wind saw that the sun had tricked him.
He was so cross that he howled and
blew over the mountains.

1

The wind thought he was stronger than the sun.
'Very well,' said the sun.
'Let us see who is the stronger.'

'I shall be first,' said the wind and
he began to blow.
But the harder he blew the more
the man wrapped his jacket around him.

The sun saw a man walking down the road.
'The one who can make the man
take off his jacket is the stronger,' said the sun.

'This is a very hot day,' said the man
and he took off his jacket.

The oak tree and the fir tree

Colour the pictures. Cut out the paragraphs.
Put them in order to tell the story.

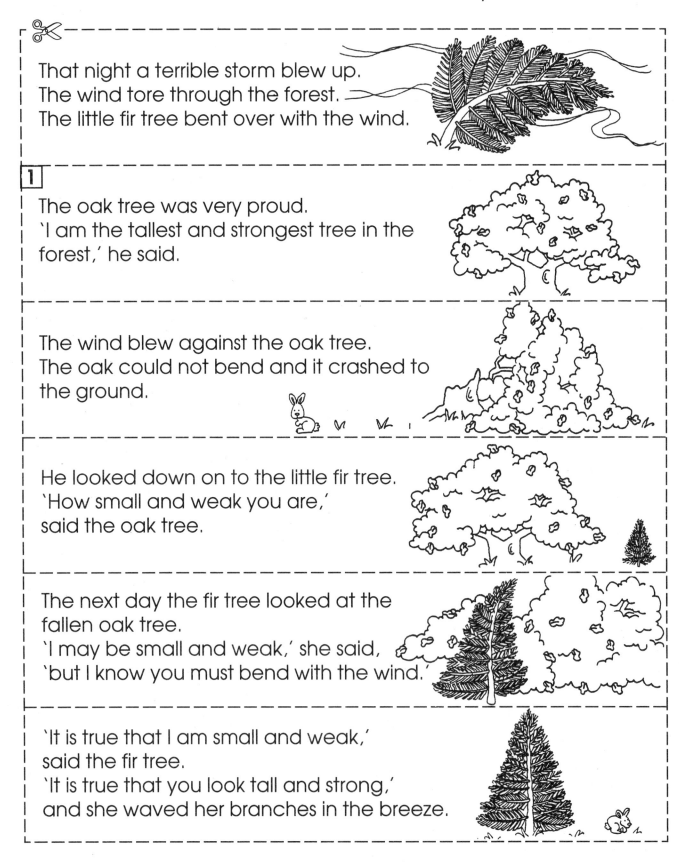

That night a terrible storm blew up.
The wind tore through the forest.
The little fir tree bent over with the wind.

1

The oak tree was very proud.
'I am the tallest and strongest tree in the forest,' he said.

The wind blew against the oak tree.
The oak could not bend and it crashed to the ground.

He looked down on to the little fir tree.
'How small and weak you are,'
said the oak tree.

The next day the fir tree looked at the fallen oak tree.
'I may be small and weak,' she said,
'but I know you must bend with the wind.'

'It is true that I am small and weak,'
said the fir tree.
'It is true that you look tall and strong,'
and she waved her branches in the breeze.